A friend...

A friend believes in you
when no one else does.
She listens when she's heard
the tale a hundred times before,
and she's there for you
when things go wrong.
She never says I told you so,
but helps you pick up the pieces
– and glues the bits together.

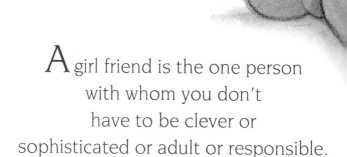

A girl friend is the one person
with whom you don't
have to be clever or
sophisticated or adult or responsible.

You make all the right noises
when I call you
with some tale of woe.
It's good to know
that someone
is always on my side.

Your face at the window,
your knock at the door,
are the best excuses I know
for setting aside routine.

A friend notices
you getting
wistful over something...
and gives it to you
as an Unbirthday surprise.

There are times in life
when we most need friends.
On standby. Ready
to do anything or go anywhere.
Thank you for doing, being,
just that.

A friend calls you up
on a sudden summer's day
and says
"Drop everything... we're going out
into the country and finding
ourselves lunch."

You double the fun.

Friends are people
who go on conspiratorial
shopping sprees together,
diving in and out of shops
totally beyond their price range,
and ending up with only
just enough money to get home.

There is such a difference
between being a little daft
all on your own
– and being a little daft together.

There are times when
I have needed to tell someone
my fear, times
when I have needed
someone to share a secret,
times when I have needed
someone to rejoice with me
over an achievement.
And those are the times
when only my friend will do.

You give me your time –
the most generous gift of all.

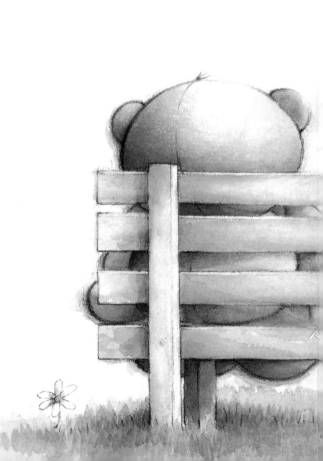